Rand al'Thor and his friends, Matrim Cauthon, Perrin Aybara, and Egwene al'Vere, have grown up in peace. To them, terrifying Trollocs and Myrddraal are creatures from a gleeman's tale. On the brink of adulthood, they are all looking forward to the annual Bel Tine festival—but their joy is ruined when a peddler arrives, bearing a tale of war.

Someone claims to be the Dragon Reborn and to be able to wield the One Power. The Aes Sedai have ridden out of Tar Valon to do battle. . . .

Visiting Emond's Field for Bel Tine are Lan, a powerful warrior, and Moiraine, a beautiful woman who gives Rand, Mat, and Perrin a silver penny each, as a token payment for work she might ask them to do during the festival.

That night, Emond's Field and the al'Thors' farm are attacked . . . by Trollocs.

Rand al'Thor's childhood has come to an end.

But the story of his life has just begun.

"Dixon's pacing is impeccable and his narration bang on. Conley's astounding, atmospheric artwork only reinforces Dixon's narrative framework. Arguably one of the best comic book adaptations on the shelves today."

—*Broken Frontier*

"All of the dialogue is straight out of the book. . . . Dixon is able to make the story flow on the page [and] all the characters look like how I imagine them. Fans of the books will be reminded of the things they enjoyed about the series in the first place."

—*Geeks of Doom*

The Wheel of Time®
Graphic Novels

Based on the Novels by Robert Jordan

New Spring:
The Graphic Novel
Robert Jordan, Chuck Dixon, Mike Miller, Harvey Tolibao

The Eye of the World:
The Graphic Novel, Volume One
Robert Jordan, Chuck Dixon, Chase Conley

Robert Jordan's

the WHEEL of TIME®

the EYE of the WORLD

Volume One

TOR®

written by
ROBERT JORDAN

adapted by
CHUCK DIXON

artwork by
CHASE CONLEY

colors by
NICOLAS CHAPUIS

original series edited by
ERNST DABEL
RICH YOUNG

lettered by
BILL TORTOLINI

thematic consultants
MARIA SIMONS
BOB KLUTTZ
ALAN ROMANCZUK

consultation
ERNST DABEL
LES DABEL

Cover art gallery by Chase Conley, Seamas Gallagher, and Jeremy Saliba
Collection edits by Rich Young
Collection design by Bill Tortolini

Dynamite Entertainment:

NICK BARRUCCI · PRESIDENT
JUAN COLLADO · CHIEF OPERATING OFFICER
JOSEPH RYBANDT · EDITOR
JOSH JOHNSON · CREATIVE DIRECTOR
RICH YOUNG · BUSINESS DEVELOPMENT
JASON ULLMEYER · GRAPHIC DESIGNER

www.dynamiteentertainment.com

Published in comic book form by Dynamic Entertainment, 155 Ninth Avenue, Suite B, Runnemede, NJ 08078. Dynamite, Dynamite Entertainment and the Dynamite Entertainment colophon are ® and © 2011 DFI. All rights reserved.

A Tor Book
Published by Tom Doherty Associates, LLC
175 Fifth Avenue
New York, NY 10010

www.tor-forge.com

Tor® is a registered trademark of Tom Doherty Associates, LLC

ISBN: 978-0-7653-3388-9

First Edition: September 2011

Printed in the United States of America

0 9 8 7 6 5 4 3 2 1

Table of
Contents

AN INTRODUCTION TO

THE WHEEL OF TIME

The world of THE WHEEL OF TIME lies in both our future
and our past, a world of kings and queens and Aes Sedai,
women who can wield *saidar*, the female half of the One Power,
which turns the Wheel and drives the universe. A world
where the war between the Light and the Shadow is fought every da
At the moment of Creation, the Creator bound the Dark One
away from the world, but more than three thousand years ago
Aes Sedai, then both men and women, unknowingly bored
into that prison outside of time. The Dark One was able to
touch the world only lightly, and the hole was eventually sealed ov
but the Dark One's taint settled on *saidin*, the male half of the Pov
Every male Aes Sedai went mad, and in the Breaking of the
World they destroyed civilization and changed the very face of ear
sinking mountains beneath the sea and bringing new seas where
land had been. Now only women bear the title Aes Sedai.
Commanded by their Amyrlin Seat and divided into seven Ajahs
named by color, they rule the great island city of Tar Valon,
where their White Tower is located.

Men still are born who can learn to channel the Power,
or worse, will channel one day whether they try to or not.
Doomed to madness, destruction, and death by the
taint on *saidin*, they are hunted down by Aes Sedai and
gentled, cut off forever from the Power for the safety of
the world. No man goes to this willingly. Even if they
survive the hunt, they seldom survive long after gentling.
For more than three thousand years, while nations and
empires rose and fell, nothing has been so feared as a man
who can channel. But for all those years there have been
the Prophecies of the Dragon, that the seals on the
Dark One's prison will weaken and he will touch the world
once more, that the Dragon, who sealed up that hole,
will be Reborn to face the Dark One again. A child,
born in sight of Tar Valon on the slopes of Dragonmount,
who will grow to be The Dragon Reborn.
The only hope of humanity in the Last Battle.

-- Robert Jordan

prologue

This far below Emond's Field, halfway to the Waterwood, trees lined the banks of the Winespring Water.

Bel Tine was past and summer not far off, and the time of shearing was here again.

All across the Two Rivers, herds from all about were brought and their wool gathered.

Egwene was not here to play.

At nine, she was carrying water for the first time.

Widow Aynal's Meadow stood empty most of the year. But now it held a good many more sheep than people.

Farmers came from all around Emond's Field for the shearing, and village folk came to help their relatives.

There were only a few other times a year when everyone gathered from all corners like this.

Though it was work to gather the sheep and clean the wool, the event took on the atmosphere of a festival.

On the pretense that the boys might be thirsty, Egwene made her way to the sheep pens.

UNNH! THIS IS THE LAST FOR NOW, MAT.

THERE'LL BE MORE SOON ENOUGH, RAND.

Among them, *Rand al'Thor.*

SHHHH!

But she did not really know Rand.

Now was as good a time as any to start learning.

I'D LIKE TO BE KING--

--THAT'S WHAT I'D LIKE TO BE.

A KING OF *SHEEP!*

The boy that everybody agreed Egwene would one day marry.

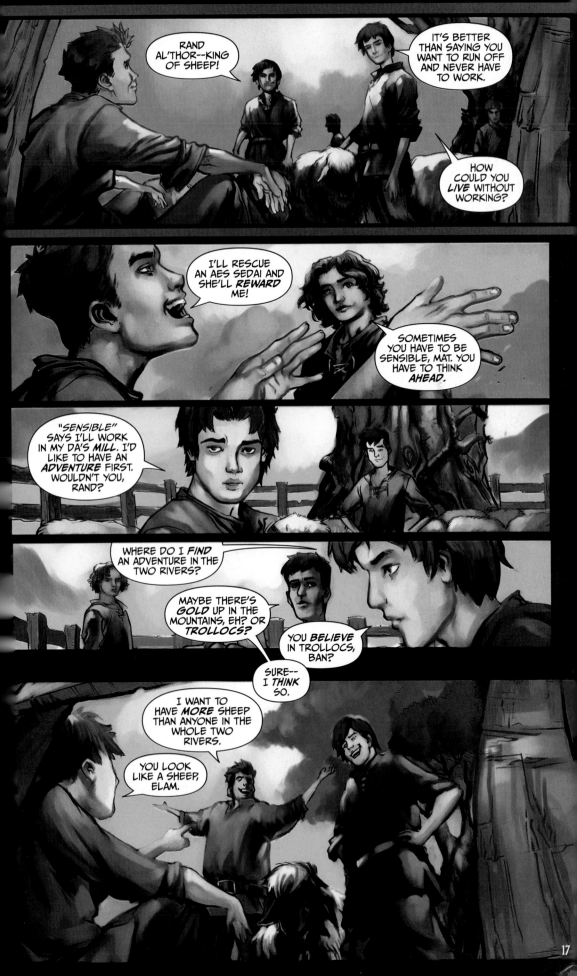

WELL, FOR NOW WE DO HAVE WORK TO DO. AND WE'D BEST BE *AT IT.*

MAT, THE *MAYOR* WANTS YOU.

ME? WHAT HAVE *I* DONE?

HE WANTS *ALL* OF YOU AND DOUBLE QUICK. I'D GET OVER TO HIM *NOW,* IF IT WAS ME.

The Mayor of the village was Egwene's father.

Surely, no one would question if she were to happen by with a drink for each.

WELL, LADS, I KNOW YOU'VE BEEN WORKING HARD. SO, I THOUGHT IT MIGHT BE TIME FOR THAT *STORY* I PROMISED YOU.

All were pleased.

Egwene's father told the best stories.

Master Tam al'Thor was Rand's father and represented the farmers of Emond's Field on the Village council.

19

WHAT DOES *"THE DRAGON"* MEAN?

SRPPLT

THE DRAGON.

IT SURELY SOUNDS *FIERCE* NOW, DOESN'T IT?

BUT IT ALL HAPPENED LONG AGO AND HAS NOTHING TO DO WITH US.

WELL, YOU'VE *HAD* YOUR BREAK AND YOUR STORY, LADS. BACK TO WORK WITH YOU.

Egwene thought about fo them. If Rand noticed her, think she was goose-brain

As if at a signal, all the ravens in the trees took off as one.

Egwene felt as if someone were staring at her back.

Someone...

22

Nothing ever happened in the Two Rivers.

Egwene would carry water all that season and into the one that followed.

She vowed to be the best water carrier *ever*.

She stopped wanting hear stories from th grown-ups, though.

And many of those stories faded and were forgotten, or half so.

The War of the Shadow?

The Breaking of the World?

Lews Therin Telamon?

How could any o that matter now

WHEEL OF TIME: DRAGONMOUNT
PROLOGUE

The palace still shook occasionally as the earth rumbled in memory.

The Dark lay heavy on the land and weighed down the hearts of men and the green things failed and hope died.

All was shattered and all memory lost and one memory above all others—of him who brought the Shadow and the Breaking of the World.

And him they named Dragon.

The dead lay everywhere.

Men and women and children.

Struck down in attempted flight by the lightning that had flashed down every corridor.

Or seized by the fire: that had stalked then

ILYENA!

MY LOVE, WHERE ARE YOU?

26

27

All slain by his own hand.

He could not bear the faces.

The pain.

Desperately he reached out for the True Source-- to the tainted *saidin*.

And he Traveled.

He was alone. As alone as any man could be while still alive.

Yet he could not escape memory.

His children's eyes. Ilyena's eyes. They pursued him through the caverns of his mind.

LIGHT!

LIGHT-- FORGIVE ME!

He drew on the One Power.

Far more than could channel

The earth heaved like a sea in a storm.

The groaning ground rose-- thrusting the burning spray ever upward.

From north and south the wind howled in, shrieking as if to aid the mountain ever skyward.

And the world was blighted and its surface blemished.

Of Lews Therin Telamon no sign remained.

Where he had stood, a mountain rose miles into the sky.

YOU CANNOT ESCAPE SO EASILY, DRAGON. IT IS NOT DONE BETWEEN US.

IT WILL NOT BE DONE UNTIL THE END OF TIME...

Then he was g

And the mountain stood alone.

Waiting

chapter one

In one age, called the Third Age by some, a *wind* rose in the Mountains of Mist.

The wind was not *the* beginning, but it was *a* beginning.

The wind blew east, out across the Sand Hills -- once the shore of a great ocean before the *breaking* of the *world*.

Down the wind flailed, into the tangled forest called the *Westwood*...

"--I EXPECT YOU'RE EAGER TO SEE EGWENE."

TAM! TAM AL'THOR!

OH, NO.

WHAT ARE WE GOING TO DO ABOUT NYNAEVE, AL'THOR?

I HAVE TO GET THIS TO BRAN AL'VERE, WIT.

SHE SAID WE'D HAVE A MILD WINTER. AND A GOOD HARVEST. AND SHE COULDN'T HAVE BEEN MORE WRONG!

WE CAN'T HAVE A WISDOM LIKE THAT FOR EMOND'S FIELD!

IT'S NOT OUR PLACE, WIT.

THE WISDOM IS WOMEN'S CIRCLE BUSINESS.

NYNAEVE AL'MEARA IS TOO YOUNG TO BE VILLAGE WISDOM, AL'THOR, AND IF THE WOMEN'S CIRCLE WON'T DO ANYTHING ABOUT IT--

WHAT BUSINESS IS OF YOURS, CONGAR?

COME ON, [D], BEFORE [I] CAN PUT YOU [TO] WORK.

DAV AND I CAUGHT AN OLD BADGER--WE'RE GOING TO LET IT LOOSE ON THE GREEN AND WATCH THE GIRLS RUN.

I DUNNO, [M]AT. I PROMISED [T]O UNLOAD THE CART.

I CAN MEET YOU LATER, THOUGH.

TOTING *BARRELS!* BURN *ME*, I'D RATHER PLAY STONES WITH MY BABY *SISTER.*

STILL, I KNOW OF BETTER THINGS THAN A *BADGER.* WE HAVE STRANGERS IN THE TWO RIVERS. LAST EVENING--

A STRANGER? WAS IT A MAN ON A BLACK HORSE? WITH A BLACK CLOAK THAT *DOESN'T MOVE* IN THE *WIND?*

[I] SAW HIM [I] THOUGHT [I WAS] THE ONLY ONE.

DON'T LAUGH, RAND, BUT HE *SCARED* ME.

I'M NOT LAUGHING. HE SCARED ME, *TOO.* IN FACT, THE WAY HE *STARED*, IT FELT LIKE-- LIKE HE WANTED TO *KILL ME.*

45

SEEING THAT RIDER, I HAVEN'T BEEN SO SCARED SINCE... I'VE *NEVER* BEEN THAT SCARED.

ME EITHER. MY FATHER THINKS I WAS JUST JUMPING AT SHADOWS.

MINE, TOO. STILL, THERE ARE TWO OF US NOW. NOBODY COULD BELIEVE WE *BOTH* IMAGINED THE *SAME THING.*

YOUR FATHER WOULD BELIEVE YOU PUT ME UP TO IT, AND *MINE*--

YOURS WOULD VERY MUCH LIKE TO SEE HIS CART *EMPTIED.*

GOOD MORNING, MATRIM. I SEE YOU'VE COME TO HELP RAND WITH THE BARRELS. GOOD LAD.

WHY GOOD MORNING, MASTER AL'THOR! *ACTUALLY,* MY DA SENT ME TO--

NO DOUBT HE DID. AND NO DOUBT, SINCE YOU'RE A LAD WHO DOES HIS CHORES RIGHT OFF, YOU'VE ALREADY FINISHED THAT TASK.

STILL, THE QUICKER YOU GET THOSE BARRELS INTO MASTER AL'VERE'S *CELLAR,* THE QUICKER YOU CAN BE OFF TO SEE THE *GLEEMAN.*

YES, ARRIVED JUST LAST NIGHT, I'M TOLD.

A *GLEEMAN?!*

LAST NIGHT? HE DOESN'T...

HE DOESN'T WEAR A *BLACK CLOAK,* DOES HE?

COURSE [C]OULD SEE [HI]S FACE.

AND HIS CLOAK WAS *GRAY.* OR GREEN? HER CLOAK WAS *BLUE,* LIKE THE SKY.

WAIT, *HER?*

OH! THEY'RE THE ONES I MEANT TO TELL YOU ABOUT, BEFORE YOU *DISTRACTED* ME.

THEY ARRIVED LAST NIGHT, TOOK ROOMS HERE AT THE INN.

HER NAME IS *MOIRAINE.* I HEARD HIM SAY IT. AND HIS IS *LAN.*

THE *WISDOM* MAY NOT LIKE HER, BUT I DO.

WHAT MAKES YOU THINK NYNAEVE DISLIKES HER?

BECAUSE THE WISDOM DISLIKES *EVERYONE.*

ALSO, THE LADY ASKED FOR DIRECTIONS THIS MORNING AND CALLED THE WISDOM *"CHILD."*

I'M SURPRISED NYNAEVE DIDN'T WHACK HER IN THE HEAD WITH A *STICK.*

=CAW=

DID YOU *EVER* SEE A RAVEN DO THAT?

chapter two

As far as Emond's Field was concerned, only one thing was as exciting as Bel Tine.

HE'S COMING!

...The coming of a peddler.

Peddlers were always a welcome sight in towns like Emond's Field. Their irregular visits provided isolated communities with a wide range of products.

Spices. Clothing and fabrics. Books. Meats from other lands.

But most important -- *news*.

WHAT NEWS FROM OUTSIDE? SPEAK UP!

DID YOU BRING FIREWORKS THIS YEAR?

THE AES SEDAI ARE *ALREADY* INTO IT.

A PARTY OF THEM HAVE RIDDEN FROM TAR VALON TO FACE THIS POTENTIAL DRAGON.

THIS HAS GONE *BEYOND* MERE NEWS FROM OUTSIDE.

AGREED. MASTER FAIN, IF YOU WOULD PLEASE JOIN THE VILLAGE COUNCIL INSIDE THE INN, WE'VE SOME QUESTIONS TO ASK.

WELL, A MUG OF HOT MULLED WINE WOULD NOT GO AMISS WITH ME RIGHT NOW.

WAIT NOW, I WANT TO HEAR WHAT HE HAS TO SAY!

ME, TOO!

MY WIFE S... ME TO BUY... YOU CAN'T J... TAKE HIM... AWAY--

AND IF YOU'D LOOK AFTER MY HORSES, I'D APPRECIATE IT.

BE *SILENT!* WHEN THE COUNCIL HAS ASKED ITS QUESTIONS, MASTER FAIN WILL RETURN TO SHARE THE NEWS WITH YOU.

AND TO SELL YOU YOUR POTS AND PINS AND WHATEVER ELSE.

UNTIL THEN, *GO HOME!*

LOOK AT OU BOYS! YOU'D THINK THE DARK ONE WAS AFTER YOU.

PEOPLE O RIDE HORSES, OU KNOW. THAT SN'T MAKE THEM NSTERS OUT OF A GLEEMAN'S TALE.

BAH!

I *WAS* SCARED OF WHOEVER IT WAS, EGWENE. IT MAY NOT HAVE BEEN A *MONSTER*, BUT IT ALSO WASN'T SIMPLY A FARMER LOOKING FOR A LOST COW. AND I--

WHAT SORT = PLACE *IS* THIS? ME DOWNSTAIRS TO OY MY PIPE AND A OF ALE, AND EVERY N IN THE COMMON OM STARES AT ME IKE I OWE HIM *MONEY.*

SOMEONE'S GRANDFATHER BEGINS RANTING AT ME ABOUT THE STORIES I *SHOULD* OR *SHOULDN'T* TELL, AND THEN A GIRL CHILD THREATENS ME WITH A GREAT *CLUB* IF I DON'T LEAVE *IMMEDIATELY.*

NOW I ASK YOU...

...IS THAT ANY WAY TO TREAT A *GLEEMAN?*

THAT'S ALL *OLD NEWS*, EVEN IN *BAERLON*... AND BAERLON IS ALWAYS THE *LAST* PLACE TO HEAR *ANYTHING.*

WELL, ALMOST THE LAST PLACE.

YAWN!

YOUR PARDON, MASTER GLEEMAN. THAT WAS OUR WISDOM, AND THE VILLAGE COUNCIL. I'M SURE THEY INTENDED NO DISCOURTESY, BUT--

THERE'S A WAR IN GHEALDAN, AND AES SEDAI ARE RIDING IN TO CONFRONT A FALSE DRAGON, AND THE COUNCIL IS TRYING TO DECIDE IF WE'RE IN DANGER HERE.

AH, I *THOUGHT* I RECOGNIZED PADAN FAIN IN THERE. NO DOUBT HE BROUGHT YOU THE NEWS OF WAR--HE HAS *ALWAYS* CARRIED BAD NEWS QUICKLY.

I THINK THERE'S MORE *RAVEN* IN HIM THAN *MAN.*

MASTER FAIN HAS COME OFTEN TO EMOND'S FIELD. HE IS ALWAYS FULL OF LAUGHTER, AND BRINGS MUCH MORE GOOD NEWS THAN BAD. I THINK YOU'RE BEING UNFAIR, MASTER GLEEMAN.

I AM SIMPLY THOM MERRILIN, CHILD, THOUGH GLEEMAN IS THE TITLE IN WHICH I GLORY.

PERHAPS YOU'D BE WILLING TO *ASSIST* ME TONIGHT? HAND ME MY FLUTE AND PROPS WHEN I ASK?

I ALWAYS TRY TO FIND THE *PRETTIEST* GIRL IN THE TOWN TO DO SO, AND I DARESAY I'VE *FOUND* HER.

OH, WHY... THANK YOU. I WOULD BE HAPPY TO.

MASTER MERRILIN... DO YOU KNOW WHAT *IS* HAPPENING IN GHEALDAN? WITH THE FALSE DRAGON AND THE AES SEDAI?

DO I LOOK LIKE A *PEDDLER*, BOY? OR A NEWSMONGER? IT'S A *WAR.* FOOLS KILLING FOOLS FOR FOOLISH CAUSES. THAT'S ENOUGH FOR *ANYONE* TO KNOW.

LOOK AT [...]LAD! YOU [...]LMOST TH[...] [...]E OF AN [...]OGIER.

A LITTLE LATER, I'LL LET YOU TRY TO PICK ME UP, BUT YOU WON'T BE ABLE TO DO IT. NOT YOU, NOR YOUR TALL FRIEND HERE, NOR ANYONE ELSE.

I THINK I CAN LIFT YOU RIGHT NOW.

NOT NOW, LATER. THERE NEED TO BE MORE FOLK TO WATCH. AN ARTIST NEEDS AN AUDIENCE.

STILL, PERHAPS THERE ARE ENOUGH HERE TO GIVE A SMALL SAMPLE.

YOU WANT *STORIES?*

STORIES I HAVE, AND I WILL MAKE THEM COME *ALIVE* FOR YOU!

TALES OF GREAT MEN AND HEROES FOR MEN BOYS. FOR WOM AND GIRLS, THE ENTIRE APTARIGIN CYCLE.

YES, I *HAVE* ALL STORIES, AND I WIL *TELL* ALL STORIES. STO OF LENN, FLYING TO THE IN AN EAGLE MADE OF F STORIES OF ELSBET, QUE ALL, AND MATARESE THE HE YES, AND TALES OF TH DRAGON... AND HIS ATTE TO FREE THE *DARK ONE.*

I WILL TELL OF THE AGE OF LEGENDS! ADVENTURES OF MEN AND WOMEN, RICH AND POOR, GREAT AND SMALL, PROUD AND HUMBLE. I WILL...

I--

MY PARDON, LADY, BUT SURELY *YOU* ARE NOT FROM THIS DISTRICT?

76

I AM SIMPLY MOIRAINE, MASTER BARD. AND YES, I AM A STRANGER HERE. A TRAVELER, LIKE YOURSELF.

THE LADY MOIRAINE COLLECTS STORIES ABOUT THE [T]WO RIVERS, THOUGH I DON'T KNOW [W]HAT EVER HAPPENED HERE THAT [YO]U COULD MAKE A STORY OF....

AH.

WELL, I TRUST YOU WILL LIKE MY STORIES, MOIRAINE.

THAT IS A MATTER OF *TASTE*, MASTER BARD. SOME STORIES I *LIKE*, AND OTHERS I DO *NOT*.

I ASSURE YOU, *NONE* OF MY STORIES WILL DISPLEASE. *ALL* WILL PLEASE AND ENTERTAIN.

PLAY THE HARP NEXT!

NO, EAT FIRE! I WANT TO SEE YOU EAT FIRE!

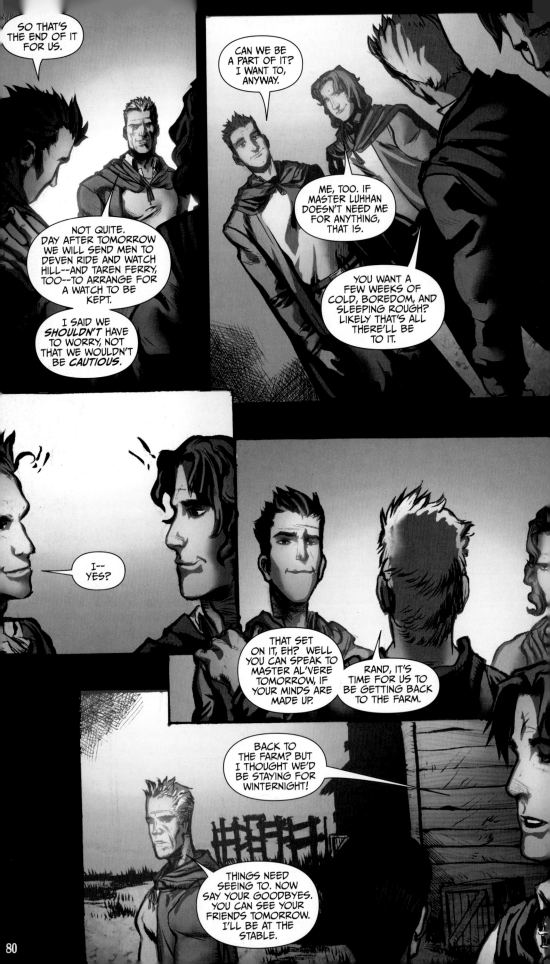

SO THAT'S THE END OF IT FOR US.

CAN WE BE A PART OF IT? I WANT TO, ANYWAY.

ME, TOO. IF MASTER LUHHAN DOESN'T NEED ME FOR ANYTHING, THAT IS.

NOT QUITE. DAY AFTER TOMORROW WE WILL SEND MEN TO DEVEN RIDE AND WATCH HILL--AND TAREN FERRY, TOO--TO ARRANGE FOR A WATCH TO BE KEPT.

I SAID WE *SHOULDN'T* HAVE TO WORRY, NOT THAT WE WOULDN'T BE *CAUTIOUS.*

YOU WANT A FEW WEEKS OF COLD, BOREDOM, AND SLEEPING ROUGH? LIKELY THAT'S ALL THERE'LL BE TO IT.

I-- YES?

THAT SET ON IT, EH? WELL YOU CAN SPEAK TO MASTER AL'VERE TOMORROW, IF YOUR MINDS ARE MADE UP.

RAND, IT'S TIME FOR US TO BE GETTING BACK TO THE FARM.

BACK TO THE FARM? BUT I THOUGHT WE'D BE STAYING FOR WINTERNIGHT!

THINGS NEED SEEING TO. NOW SAY YOUR GOODBYES. YOU CAN SEE YOUR FRIENDS TOMORROW. I'LL BE AT THE STABLE.

chapter three

The sun stood halfway down from its noonday high by the time the cart reached the farmhouse.

DON'T THINK THE [BLAC]K-CLOAKED [M]AN CAME [H]ERE...

THE SHEEP WOULDN'T BE SO SETTLED IF *THAT ONE* HAD BEEN AROUND.

I SUPPOSE HE DIDN'T. STILL, ALL THIS TALK ABOUT MEN AND HORSES I CAN'T SEE OR HEAR JUST MAKES ME LOOK CROSSWAYS AT *EVERYTHING.*

RAND! LET'S WASH UP, LAD, AND SEE ABOUT SOME SUPPER.

I'VE ALREADY CARRIED IN THE WATER FOR HOT BATHS BEFORE SLEEP.

ANYTHING HOT SOUNDS GOOD TO ME.

KrRACK

WOULD YOU CARE TO MAKE A SMALL WAGER ON THAT?

AND SLEEP, TOO. I JUST MIGHT SLEEP RIGHT THROUGH FESTIVAL.

--BUT I [DO]N'T WANT [to risk] CALLING OUT. [THE] TROLLOCS [might] HEAR [us] LIKE A [dog?]. MAYBE [B]ETTER.

BUT TROLLOCS ARE JUST... ARE YOU SURE?

I MEAN... TROLLOCS?

I'M SURE. THOUGH WHAT BROUGHT THEM TO THE TWO RIVERS...

I NEVER SAW ONE BEFORE TONIGHT, BUT I'VE TALKED WITH MEN WHO HAVE, SO I KNOW A LITTLE. MAYBE ENOUGH TO KEEP US ALIVE.

[LI]STEN [CL]OSELY.

A TROLLOC CAN SEE BETTER THAN A MAN IN THE DARK, BUT BRIGHT LIGHTS BLIND THEM. FOR A TIME, AT LEAST.

THAT MAY BE THE ONLY REASON WE GOT AWAY FROM SO MANY.

SOME CAN TRACK BY SCENT OR SOUND, BUT THEY'RE SAID TO BE LAZY. IF WE CAN KEEP OUT OF THEIR HANDS LONG ENOUGH, THEY SHOULD GIVE UP.

[IN T]HE STORIES, [TRO]LLOCS HATE AND SERVE [T]HE DARK ONE.

DO YOU THINK THEY'RE STILL HUNTING US?

IF ANYTHING BELONGS IN THE SHEPHERD OF THE NIGHT'S FLOCKS, LAD, IT IS TROLLOCS. THEY KILL FOR THE PLEASURE OF KILLING, AND THEY CAN'T BE TRUSTED UNLESS THEY'RE AFRAID OF YOU...

AND EVEN THEN, NOT FAR.

99

WHERE ARE YOU GOING?
WE NEED THE CART. AND BLANKETS. REST. I'LL BE BACK.
BE CAREFUL.
I WILL BE.

chapter four

It was difficult for Rand to see in the moonlight, but Tam's wound seemed to be only a shallow gash along the ribs.

Trollocs. Creatures from a gleeman's tale, coming out of the night to bash in the door.

And a Fade as well! Things like that never happened.

Rand knew he couldn't just sit around, frozen like a rabbit that had seen a hawk's shadow.

But knowing what to do, even getting on with it, did not stop him from being afraid.

When the Trollocs came back, they would surely begin searching the forest for *some* trace of the people who had escaped them.

OOHHH...

SKRICH

And who knew what a Fade would --or could--do?

YOU HAVE TO KEEP *QUIET.*

THE *TROLLOCS* WILL BE BACK.

YOU'RE STILL LOVELY, *KARI.* STILL LOVELY AS A GIRL.

Rand's mother had been dead for *fifteen years.*

MOTHER WANTS YOU TO--

--*KARI* WANTS YOU TO BE *QUIET.*

HERE. DRINK THIS.

If Tam believed she was alive, the fever must be worse than Rand had thought.

How could Tam be kept from speaking, now that silence meant life?

Three blankets, woven around the shafts cut from the cart, formed a makeshift litter.

Rand would only be able to carry one end of the litter, and that would make the journey difficult on Tam.

SHRRK

But it would have to do.

The best plan was to head for the Quarry Road and follow it to Emond's Field.

The danger would almost certainly be greater along the road, but Tam would receive no help at all if they were lost in the woods in the dark.

In the darkness, Rand was nearly out on the Quarry Road before he knew it.

Nearly on the road. Nearly *out* in the *open*.

Rand's throat tightened. Traveling through the trees was difficult, but going out onto the road would be *madness*.

The idea was to reach the village *without* meeting any Trollocs. Without even seeing any.

He had to assume the Trollocs were still hunting them, and sooner or later, they'd realize the two had set off for the village.

That was the most likely place to go, and the Quarry Road the most likely route.

Even under cover of forest, Rand was closer to the road than he like

Moonlight filtering through the bare branches gave just enough illumination to fool Rand's eyes into thinking they saw what was underfoot.

ots threatened to trip n at every step. Brambles agged at him. Sudden dips rises had Rand stumbling th almost every stride.

Tam's mutterings broke into a sharp groan whenever one of the shafts of the litter bumped too quickly over root or rock.

AH!

HRR...

WHOMP

But still Rand kept on.

Uncertainty made him peer into the darkness until his eyes burned.

Every scrape of branch against branch brought him to a halt.

Only when he was sure it was wind would he go on.

Even with weariness creeping into his arms and legs, reminding him that he had been up since dawn, working for most of the day... and had had nothing to eat since Mistress al'Vere's honeycakes, Rand continued.

Un

123

TH DOMP
TH DOMP

TH DOMP
TH DOMP

Wavering shadows slowly resolved themselves into a horse and rider... followed up the road by tall, bulky shapes trotting to keep up with the animal.

...never even considered they might be villagers ...ing to help.

...e knew what was coming. He ...ould feel it, even before they ...ere close enough for the ...oonlight to reveal them.

Rand counted twenty Trollocs following the Dark Rider as they ran past.

What kind of man would dare turn his back on so many Trollocs? Or one, for that matter.

The trotting column disappeared westward, but Rand remained where he was – not moving a muscle except to breathe.

Something told him to be certain, *absolutely certain*, they were gone before he moved.

125

This time, the horse made no sound at all.

n eerie silence the dark rider eturned, his shadowy mount stopping every few steps.

The rider peered into the forest, and despite the cold wind, sweat beaded on Rand's face.

The horse moved on down the road, a few silent steps and stop.

Rand did not take his eyes off the rider for a second.

Abruptly, the shadowy mount rushed back, passing Rand in a silent gallop.

The rider looked only ahead as he raced westward. Toward the Mountains of Mist. Toward the *farm*.

chapter five

HERE, TOO. HERE, TOO. WE MAY HAVE BEEN LUCKIER THAN ANYONE HAS A RIGHT TO BE, IF YOU CAN CREDIT IT.

HE NEEDS THE WISDOM. NOW *WHERE* THE LIGHT IS SHE?

EGWENE!

WHAT? I--OH, *NO*, RAND, NOT YOUR *FATHER?*

COME, I'LL TAKE YOU TO *NYNAEVE.*

ALL THE STORIES ARE REAL.

SO IT SEEMS, LAD. SO IT SEEMS.

COME ON, THEN.

137

GOING INSIDE? OF COURSE, OF COURSE.

DON'T YOU WORRY, BOY. YOUR WISDOM WILL TAKE CARE OF HIM. I'VE WATCHED HER WORK, SINCE LAST NIGHT, AND SHE HAS A DEFT TOUCH AND SURE SKILL.

COULD BE A LOT WORSE. SOME DIED LAST NIGHT. NOT MANY, PERHAPS, BUT ANY AT ALL ARE TOO MANY FOR ME.

OLD FAIN JUST DISAPPEARD, AND THAT'S THE WORST OF ALL. TROLLOCS WILL EAT ANYTHING.

YOU SHOULD THANK THE LIGHT YOUR FATHER'S STILL HERE AND ALIVE FOR THE WISDOM TO HEAL.

AHEM-- THE DOOR?

OH!

143

...IF THE MAYOR KNEW WHO SCRAWLED THE *DRAGON'S FANG* ON HIS DOOR.

IT'S PROBABLY THE WORK OF ONE OF THE CONGARS, OR A COPLIN. THOUGH THE LIGHT ALONE KNOWS WHICH.

...MEONE 'S NOT TO ...KE HIM ...YMORE.

OR MAYBE IT'S *HIS GUESTS* THEY DON'T LIKE.

THAT FOOL DARL COPLIN SPENT HALF THE NIGHT DEMANDING I PUT MISTRESS MOIRAINE AND MASTER LAN OUT OF THE INN, OUT OF THE *VILLAGE*...

...AS IF THERE WOULD BE ANY VILLAGE AT ALL *LEFT* WITHOUT THEM.

WHAT DID THEY *DO*?

AN AES SEDAI? SHE *CAN'T* BE. I *TALKED* TO HER. SHE ISN'T... SHE DOESN'T....

IT'S STILL ALMOST *TOO MUCH* TO BELIEVE.

AN *AES SEDAI* IN EMOND'S FIELD. AND MASTER LAN IS A *WARDER*.

SWACK

DID YOU THINK THEY WORE *SIGNS*? "AES SEDAI" PAINTED ACROSS THEIR BACKS, AND MAYBE "DANGER, STAY AWAY"?

I--

AES SEDAI! I'M AN OLD *FOOL*, AND LOSING MY *WITS*!

THERE'S A *CHANCE*, RAND, IF YOU'RE WILLING TO *TAKE* IT. I CAN'T TELL YOU TO DO IT, AND I DON'T KNOW IF I'D HAVE THE *NERVE*, IF IT WERE ME.

A CHANCE? I'LL TAKE *ANY* CHANCE, IF IT'LL HELP.

AES SEDAI CAN *HEAL*, RAND. BURN ME, LAD, YOU'VE HEARD THE STORIES. THEY CAN CURE WHERE MEDICINES *FAIL*.

GLEEMAN, YOU SHOULD HAVE REMEMBERED BETTER THAN I. GLEEMEN'S TALES ARE FULL OF THE AES SEDAI. WHY DIDN'T YOU SPEAK UP?

I'M A STRANGER HERE, AND GOODM... COPLIN ISN'T THE O... ONE WHO WANTS NOTHING TO DO WI... AES SEDAI.

BEST THE IDEA CA... FROM *YOU*...

AN AES SEDAI...

IT'S THE ONLY CHANCE I CAN SEE, BUT IT'S STILL NO SMALL DECISION. I CANNOT MAKE IT FOR YOU.

BUT I HAVE SEEN ONLY *GOOD* FROM MISTRESS MOIRAINE--MOIRAINE SEDAI, I SHOULD CALL HER.

SOME OF THE STORIES ARE EXAGGERATED IN A WAY. SOME OF THEM. BESIDES, BOY, WHAT *CHOICE* DO YOU HAVE?

NONE.

I'LL... I'LL GO TO HER.

THE OTHER SIDE OF THE BRIDGES, WHERE THEY ARE... *DISPOSING* OF THE DEAD TROLLOCS. BE *CAREFUL*, BOY--

I AM *AFRAID*, LAN. I THOUGHT WE HAD GAINED A MARCH, BUT WE MAY BE FURTHER BEHIND THAN EVER.

MISTRESS *MOIRAINE*! I MEAN, MOIRAINE *SEDAI*.

A LITTLE MORE *LIGHT* IN THE *DARKNESS*.

HOW ARE YOUR *DREAMS*, RAND AL'THOR?

MY *DREAMS*?

A NIGHT LIKE *THAT* CAN GIVE A MAN BAD DREAMS, RAND.

IF YOU HAVE *NIGHTMARES*, YOU *MUST* TELL ME OF THEM. I CAN *HELP* WITH BAD DREAMS, *SOMETIMES*.

chapter six

HE WAS THERE. MUST HAVE BEEN. HIS CLOAK DID NOT GET SINGED IN FRONT OF A FIREPLACE.

MY FATHER?

LEAVE ME WITH HIM, MASTER AL'VERE. THERE IS *NOTHING* YOU CAN DO NOW EXCEPT GET IN MY *WAY*.

FINE, THEN.

COME ALONG, BOY. LET US LEAVE MOIRAINE SEDAI TO HER... UH....

CAN I *STAY*? I'LL KEEP OUT OF YOUR--

YES, YES.

WELL, THERE'S PLENTY YOU CAN HELP ME WITH DOWN-STAIRS. BEFORE YOU KNOW IT, TAM WILL BE SHOUTING FOR HIS PIPE AND A MUG OF ALE.

WAIT...

SIT OVER THERE. YOU TOO, LAN.

YOU MAY TALK IF YOU WISH, BUT DO IT *QUIETLY*.

YOU GO, MASTER AL'VERE. THIS IS A *SICK ROOM*, NOT A *GATHERING HALL*. SEE THAT I AM NOT *DISTURBED*.

THAT'S A FINE WEAPON YOU WEAR. IS THERE BY ANY CHANCE A *HERON* ON THE BLADE AS WELL?

YES, THERE IS. WHAT IS SHE DOING?

HM. I'D NOT HAVE THOUGHT TO FIND A HERON-MARK SWORD IN A PLACE LIKE *THIS*.

IT BELONGS TO MY FATHER. HE BOUGHT IT SOME TIME AGO.

STRANGE THING FOR A *SHEEPHERDER* TO BUY.

THAT BLADE MUST HAVE TRAVELED A *STRANGE* ROAD TO END UP IN THE *TWO RIVERS*.

THE MAYOR SAID THE ONLY REASON THERE'S ANYTHING LEFT OF THE VILLAGE IS BECAUSE OF YOU AND HER.

IF YOU HAD BEEN TOLD ABOUT A MAN IN THE WOODS... A MAN WHO COULD MAKE PEOPLE *AFRAID* JUST BY *LOOKING* AT HIM... A MAN WHOSE HORSE MADE NO SOUND, AND THE WIND WOULDN'T TOUCH HIS CLOAK...

...COULD YOU AND [TH]E SEDAI HAVE STOPPED [HI]F YOU'D KNOWN ABOUT [HI]M? IF YOU'D BEEN WARNED?

...NOT WITHOUT A *DOZEN* OF MY SISTERS.

HAD I KNOWN WHEN I LEFT *TAR VALON* THAT I WOULD HAVE FOUND TROLLOCS AND MYRDDRAAL HERE... THERE IS ONLY SO MUCH ONE PERSON CAN DO, EVEN WHEN CALLING ON THE *ONE POWER*.

159

IT *STILL* WOULD HAVE BEEN GOOD TO *KNOW.* WHEN DID YOU *SEE* HIM, *EXACTLY,* AND *WHERE?*

THAT'S OF NO CONSEQUENCE NOW. I'LL *NOT* HAVE THE BOY THINKING HE IS TO BLAME *WHEN* HE IS *NOT.*

I AM AS MUCH TO BLAME. THAT ACCURSED RAVEN YESTERDAY, THE WAY IT *BEHAVED,* SHOULD HAVE *WARNED* ME.

I WAS *OVERCONFIDENT* TO THE POINT OF *ARROGANCE,* SURE THE *DARK ONE'S* TOUCH COULD NOT HAVE SPREAD SO *FAR.*

THE *RAVEN?* I DON'T *UNDER-STAND.*

CARRION EATERS.

THE *DARK ONE'S* MINIONS OFTEN FIND SPIES AMONG CREATURES THAT *FEED* ON *DEATH.* RAVENS AND CROWS, MOSTLY. *RATS,* IN THE CITIES..

TROLLOC WEAPONS ARE FORGED IN THE VALLEY CALLED *THAKAN'DAR*, ON THE SLOPES OF *SHAYOL GHUL* ITSELF. SOME OF THEM TAKE A *TAINT* FROM THAT PLACE, A STAIN OF *EVIL* IN THE METAL.

NOT YET.

NNNMM...

YOU'VE DONE IT!

THOSE TAINTED BLADES CAUSE WOUNDS THAT WILL NOT HEAL UNAIDED, DEADLY FEVERS, STRANGE SICKNESSES MEDICINES CANNOT TOUCH...

...HAVE SOOTHED YOUR FATHER'S PAIN, BUT THE TAINT IS STILL IN HIM. LEFT ALONE, IT WILL GROW AGAIN AND CONSUME HIM.

...T YOU ...ON'T ...VE IT ...ONE.

I WILL NOT.

I *AM* VERY TIRED, RAND, AND I HAVE HAD NO CHANCE TO REST SINCE LAST NIGHT.

ORDINARILY IT WOULD NOT MATTER, BUT FOR *THIS* KIND OF HURT...

THIS IS AN *ANGREAL*.

SO *FEW* REMAIN, THE *AMYRLIN SEAT* ALMOST DID NOT ALLOW ME TO TAKE THIS ONE. IT IS WELL FOR EMOND'S FIELD, AND YOUR FATHER, THAT SHE DID GIVE HER PERMISSION... BUT YOU MUST *NOT* HOPE TOO *MUCH*.

YOU CAN HELP HIM. I *KNOW* YOU CAN.

WE SHALL SEE.

N-NOT EXACTLY. *IT* ALKED TO *ME*. IT SAID IT OULDN'T HURT ME, THAT E *MYRDDRAAL* WANTED TO *TALK* TO ME.

THEN IT TRIED TO *KILL* ME. I KILLED IT NSTEAD. BY *ACCIDENT*, EALLY. IT JUMPED AT ME, AND I HAD THE *SWORD* IN MY *HAND*....

EVEN SO, *THAT* IS SOMETHING TO SPEAK OF, SHEEPHERDER. UNTIL LAST NIGHT THERE WERE FEW MEN SOUTH OF THE BORDERLANDS WHO COULD SAY THEY HAD *SEEN* A TROLLOC, MUCH LESS *KILLED* ONE.

AND FEWER STILL WHO HAVE SLAIN A TROLLOC *ALONE* AND *UNAIDED*.

IT IS *DONE*, RAND. LAN, HELP ME UP.

WITH *REST*, YES. HE WILL BE AS GOOD AS EVER. THE TAINT IS *GONE*.

HE WILL BE ALL RIGHT NOW?

N *NEVER* REPAY YOU. BUT NG I CAN DO FOR YOU, AS AS IT DOES NOT HURT THE LAGE OR MY FRIENDS, I *WILL*.

IF YOU THINK IT *NECESSARY*. I WOULD LIKE TO TALK WITH YOU ANYWAY... YOU WILL NO DOUBT LEAVE AT THE SAME TIME *WE* DO, AND WE CAN SPEAK AT LENGTH THEN.

LEAVE!?

TWO FARMS
ERE ATTACKED:
OURS AND THE
AYBARAS'.

HERE IN EMOND'S FIELD, THEY STRUCK FIRST AT THE FORGE, THE BLACKSMITH'S HOUSE, AND MASTER CAUTHON'S HOUSE.

THAT-- THAT'S CRAZY.

NOT CRAZY, RAND. *PURPOSEFUL.* THE TROLLOCS DID NOT COME TO EMOND'S FIELD BY HAPPENSTANCE.

THEY KNEW XACTLY WHAT-- , RATHER, *WHO* THEY WERE AFTER.

THE TROLLOCS CAME TO KILL OR PTURE *YOUNG MEN* A *CERTAIN AGE* WHO IVE NEAR EMOND'S FIELD.

MY AGE? *LIGHT!* MAT.

WHAT ABOUT *PERRIN?*

ALIVE AND WELL, IF A TRIFLE SOOTY.

BAN CRAWE AND LEM THANE?

WERE NEVER IN ANY DANGER. AT LEAST NO MORE THAN ANYONE ELSE.

BUT THEY SAW THE RIDER, TOO, THE FADE, AND THEY'RE THE SAME AGE I AM! THEY--

IT TOOK A *HUGE* EFFORT TO BRING SO *MANY* TROLLOCS SO FAR WITHOUT RAISING A CRY. I WISH I KNEW HOW THEY DID IT.

DO YOU REALLY THINK THEY WENT TO ALL THAT TROUBLE JUST TO BURN A FEW HOUSES?

AND THEY *WILL* BE BACK.

THAT'S WHY I-- WE HAVE TO LEAVE, T IT? THE TROLLOCS ON'T COME BACK IF WE'RE NOT HERE.

WE COULD GO TO BAERLON, I SUPPOSE. OR EVEN CAEMLYN. I'VE HEARD THERE ARE MORE PEOPLE IN CAEMLYN THAN IN THE WHOLE TWO RIVERS. WE'D BE SAFE THERE.

I USED TO DAYDREAM ABOUT SEEING CAEMLYN, BUT NEVER LIKE THIS.

I WOULD NOT COUNT ON CAEMLYN SAFETY. IF THE MYRDDRAAL YOU BADLY ENOUGH, THEY L FIND A WAY. WALLS ARE A POOR BAR TO A HALFMAN.

THERE IS A PLACE OF SAFETY...

IN *TAR VALON* YOU WOULD BE AMONG AES SEDAI AND WARDERS. EVEN DURING THE TROLLOC WARS, THE FORCES OF THE DARK ONE FEARED TO ATTACK THE SHINING WALLS.

AND TAR VALON HOLDS ALL THE KNOWLEDGE WE AES SEDAI HAVE GATHERED SINCE THE TIME OF MADNESS. SOME FRAGMENTS EVEN DATE FROM THE AGE OF LEGENDS.

IN TAR VALON, IF ANYWHERE, YOU WILL BE ABLE TO LEARN WHY THE MYRDDRAAL WANT YOU. WHY THE FATHER OF LIES WANTS YOU.

THAT I CAN PROMISE.

167

A journey to Tar Valon was almost beyond thinking. A journey to a place where Rand would be **surrounded** by Aes Sedai.

Of course, Moiraine had healed Tam -- or it looked as if she had, at least-- but there were all those stories. It was uncomfortable enough to be in a room with one Aes Sedai, but a city full of them...

...And she still had n⟨ demanded her price There was **always** price, the stories sa⟨

HOW LONG WILL MY FATHER SLEEP? I...

I HAVE TO TELL HIM SHOULDN'T J WAKE AND F ME **GONE**

IT IS UNLIKELY HE WILL AWAKE BEFORE WE DEPART. I MEAN TO GO SOON AFTER FULL DARK.

EVEN A SINGLE DAY OF DELAY MAY BE **FATAL**. IT WOULD BE BEST IF YOU LEAVE HIM A NOTE.

IN THE **NIGHT**? I -- IN THAT CASE, I'D BETTER GO FIND MAT AND PERRIN....

I WILL ATTEND TO **THAT**.

I WILL HAVE MISTRESS AL'VERE BRING YOU SOMETHING TO EAT, AND THEN YOU NEED TO **SLEEP**. THIS WILL BE A HARD JOURNEY, EVEN IF YOU ARE **RESTED**.

The mountain was taller than any Rand had seen in the Mountains of Mist, as black as the loss of all hope. The bleak stone spire, a dagger stabbing at the heavens, was the source of Rand's desolation.

He had never seen it before, but he *knew* it... the memory of it flashed away like quicksilver when he tried to touch it, but the memory was there.

He *knew* it was there.

Unseen fingers touched him, pulled at his arms and legs, trying to draw him to the mountain.

Ghostly strings entwined around his heart, pulling him, calling him to the spire mountain.

...nd felt his will draining away ...e water out of a holed ...cket. Just a little longer and ... would go where he was ...lled. He would obey.

A voice, a *familiar* voice, whispered in the stillness of his mind:

Abruptly, he discovered *another* emotion... *anger*.

SERVE ME!

THE LIGHT *CONSUME YOU, SHAI'TAN!*

SERVE ME.

WHA--?

Like the chasm, the field abruptly vanished. Now smiling people walked through village streets, dressed in so many colors they reminded him of a meadow full of wildflowers.

Some of the villagers spoke to Rand, but he could not understand them, though their words were tantalizingly familiar.

But their faces were friendly, and the people gestured him onward, toward shining, silver-streaked walls and towers...toward the safety he knew waited there.

...erywhere were smiling faces. ...all children strewed Rand's ...th with flower petals -- for a ...oment, he wondered who the ...ention was meant for.

But it was for him, and all was as it should be.

In the back of his mind, Rand could hear a voice saying, *"This is your destiny."*

"...Your *destiny.*"

CREEEEAK

Rand entered the tower without hesitation. *This* was where he *belonged*.

It was his destiny.

WHA--?

SLAM!

RAND AL'THOR

...WE HAVE BEEN *WAITING* FOR YOU...

THERE YOU ARE, BOY. MARIN *SAID* YOU WERE HERE, BUT I COULDN'T EVEN SIT UP TO SEE.

NOOO!

CAN I GET YOU SOMETHING TO EAT? MISTRESS AL'VERE LEFT A TRAY...

SAY YOUR GOODBYES *QUICKLY,* SHEEPHERDER, AND COME. THERE MAY BE TROUBLE.

TROUBLE?

SHE FED ME ALREADY, IF YOU CAN CALL IT THAT. WOULDN'T LET ME HAVE ANYTHING BUT BROTH.

HOW CAN A MAN AVOID BAD DREAMS WITH NOTHING BUT BROTH IN HIS...

JUST *HURRY!*

177

chapter seven

181

182

...I'D BE SHOCKED TO SEE ANY MEMBER OF THE VILLAGE COUNCIL HERE, BUT YOU MOST OF ALL. YOUR ARM WOULD STILL BE HANGING AT YOUR SIDE, A USELESS MASS OF BURNS AND BRUISES, IF NOT FOR *HER*.

IF YOU HAVE NO *GRATITUDE*, HAVE YOU NO *SHAME*?

I CANNOT DENY WHAT SHE DID. SHE HELPED ME AND OTHERS.

BUT SHE'S AN *AES SEDAI*, BRAN. IF THOSE TROLLOCS DIDN'T COME BECAUSE OF *HER*, WHY *DID* THEY COME? WE WANT NO PART OF AES SEDAI IN THE TWO RIVERS. LET THEM KEEP *THEIR* TROUBLES *AWAY* FROM US.

WE WANT NO AES SEDAI TROUBLES!

SEND HER AWAY!

NOW, LOOK--

FORGOTTEN WHO WE ARE? WE ARE WHO WE ALWAYS HAVE BEEN. HONEST FARMERS AND SHEPHERDS AND CRAFTSMEN. TWO RIVERS FOLK.

TO THE SOUTH LIES THE RIVER YOU CALL THE WHITE RIVER, BUT FAR TO THE EAST OF HERE, MEN STILL CALL IT BY ITS RIGHTFUL NAME:

"MANETHERENDRELLE."

"TWO THOUSAND YEARS AGO MANETHERENDRELLE FLOWED BY THE WALLS OF A MOUNTAIN CITY SO LOVELY TO BEHOLD THAT OGIER STONEMASONS CAME TO STARE IN WONDER."

"FARMS AND VILLAGES COVERED THIS REGION, AND WHAT YOU NOW CALL THE FOREST OF SHADOWS, AND BEYOND. BUT ALL OF THOSE FOLK THOUGHT OF THEMSELVES AS THE PEOPLE OF THE MOUNTAIN HOME, THE PEOPLE OF MANETHEREN."

"THEIR KING WAS AEMON AL CAAR AL THORIN, AND ELDRENE WAS HIS QUEEN."

"AEMON, A MAN SO FEARLESS THAT THE GREATEST COMPLIMENT FOR COURAGE ANY COULD GIVE, EVEN HIS ENEMIES, WAS TO SAY A MAN HAD AEMON'S HEART."

"ELDRENE, SO BEAUTIFUL IT IS SAID THE FLOWERS BLOOMED TO MAKE HER SMILE."

"BRAVERY AND BEAUTY AND WISDOM AND A LOVE THAT DEATH COULD NOT SUNDER. WEEP, IF YOU HAVE A HEART, FOR THE LOSS OF THEM, FOR THE LOSS OF EVEN THEIR MEMORY."

"WEEP FOR THE LOSS OF THEIR BLOOD."

"THEY WERE FAR AWAY, THE MEN OF MANETHEREN, WHEN WORD CAME THAT A TROLLOC ARMY WAS MARCHING AGAINST THEIR HOME."

"WITHOUT HESITATION OR THOUGHT FOR THE DISTANCE THEY MUST TRAVEL, THEY MARCHED FROM THE FIELD OF VICTORY, STILL COVERED IN DUST AND SWEAT AND BLOOD. DAY AND NIGHT THEY MARCHED. THEY MOVED AS THOUGH THEIR FEET HAD WINGS."

"AND WHEN THE DARK ONE'S ARMIES SWOOPED DOWN UPON THE LAND OF MANETHEREN..."

"...THE MEN OF THE MOUNTAIN HOME STOOD BEFORE IT, WITH THEIR BACKS TO THE TARENDRELLE."

"THE HOST THAT FACED THE MEN OF MANETHEREN WAS ENOUGH TO DAUNT THE BRAVEST HEART."

"RAVENS BLACKENED THE SKY; TROLLOCS AND THEIR HUMAN ALLIES BLACKENED THE LAND. TROLLOCS AND DARKFRIENDS IN THE TENS OF TENS OF THOUSANDS, AND DREADLORDS TO COMMAND."

"AT NIGHT, THEIR COOKFIRES OUTNUMBERED THE STARS..."

"..AND DAWN REVEALED THE BANNER OF BA'ALZAMON AT THEIR HEAD."

"BA'ALZAMON, HEART OF THE DARK. AN ANCIENT NAME FOR THE FATHER OF LIES. IT SENT A CHILL INTO THE SOULS OF THE MEN WHO FACED IT."

"YET THEY KNEW WHAT THEY MUST DO."

"THEY MUST KEEP THAT HOST FROM THE MOUNTAIN HOME. AEMON HAD SENT OUT MESSENGERS, AND AID WAS PROMISED IF THEY COULD HOLD FOR BUT THREE DAYS AT THE TARENDRELLE."

"HOLD FOR THREE DAYS AGAINST ODDS THAT SHOULD OVERWHELM THEM IN THE FIRST HOUR."

"YET SOMEHOW, THROUGH BLOODY ASSAULT AND DESPERATE DEFENSE, THEY HELD THROUGH AN HOUR."

"AND THE SECOND HOUR."

"AND THE THIRD."

"FOR THREE DAYS THEY FOUGHT, AND THOUGH THE LAND BECAME A BUTCHER'S YARD, NO CROSSING OF THE TARENDRELLE DID THEY YIELD."

"BY THE THIRD NIGHT, NO HELP HAD COME, AND NO MESSENGERS, AND THEY FOUGHT ON ALONE. FOR SIX DAYS. FOR NINE."

"AND ON THE TENTH DAY, AEMON KNEW THE BITTER TASTE OF BETRAYAL."

"NO HELP WAS COMING, AND THEY COULD HOLD THE RIVER CROSSINGS NO MORE."

"DRIVEN BY GRIEF, SHE REACHED OUT TO THE TRUE SOURCE, AND HURLED THE **ONE POWER** AT THE TROLLOC ARMY."

"IN THE PASSING OF A BREATH, THE DREADLORDS AND GENERALS OF THE DARK ONE'S HOST BURST INTO FLAME. FIRE CONSUMED THEIR BODIES AND TERROR CONSUMED THEIR JUST-VICTORIOUS ARMY."

"WHEN ALL WAS SAID AND DONE, **NONE** WERE LEFT ALIVE WHO DID MURDER AT **AEMON'S FIELD.**"

"BUT THE PRICE WAS HIGH FOR MANETHEREN. ELDRENE HAD DRAWN TO HERSELF MORE OF THE ONE POWER THAN ANY HUMAN COULD HOPE TO WIELD UNAIDED."

"AS THE ENEMY DIED, SO DID SHE DIE, AND THE FIRES THAT CONSUMED HER CONSUMED THE EMPTY CITY OF MANETHEREN, EVEN THE STONES OF IT, DOWN TO THE LIVING ROCK OF THE MOUNTAINS."

"YET THE PEOPLE HAD BEEN SAVED."

NEVER AGAIN DID MANETHEREN RISE.

ITS SOARING SPIRES AND SPLASHING FOUNTAINS BECAME AS A DREAM THAT SLOWLY FADED FROM THE MINDS OF ITS PEOPLE. BUT THEY, AND THEIR CHILDREN, AND THEIR CHILDREN'S CHILDREN, HELD THE LAND.

THEY HELD IT UNTIL, TODAY, THERE IS YOU.

WEEP FOR MANETHEREN. WEEP FOR WHAT IS LOST...

...FOREVER.

I DON'T KNOW ABOUT YOUR STORY...

...I'M NO THORN TO THE DARK ONE'S FOOT, NOR EVER LIKELY TO BE, NEITHER.

BUT MY WIL IS WALKING BECAUSE OF YOU, AND FOR THAT, I AM ASHAMED TO BE HERE.

I DON'T KNOW IF YOU CAN FORGIVE ME, BUT WHETHER YOU WILL OR NO I'LL BE GOING.

AND FOR ME, YOU CAN STAY IN EMOND'S FIELD AS LONG AS YOU LIKE.

...ater....

I COULDN'T GO OFF WITHOUT LETTING HIM KNOW.

WHAT IS *DONE* IS ALREADY *WOVEN* INTO THE *PATTERN*.

LAN?

THE HORSES ARE READY.

WE HAVE ENOUGH PROVISIONS TO REACH BAERLON WITH SOME TO SPARE. WE CAN LEAVE AT ANY TIME. I SUGGEST *NOW.*

NOT WITHOUT *ME!*

I HAVE EVERYTHING I NEED HERE, INCLUDING FOOD, AND I WILL *NOT* BE LEFT BEHIND.

I'LL PROBABLY NEVER GET ANOTHER CHANCE TO SEE THE WORLD OUTSIDE THE TWO RIVERS.

HOW DID YOU FIND OUT WE WERE LEAVING?

ANYWAY, *CAN'T GO* US. WE A LEAVING FO FUN OF I' TROLLO(AFTER

FIRST I SAW MAT CREEPING ABOUT, TRYING *HARD* NOT TO BE NOTICED. THEN I SAW PERRIN TRYING TO HIDE THAT ABSURD GREAT *AXE* UNDER HIS CLOAK.

I KNEW LAN HAD BOUGHT A HORSE, AND IT SUDDENLY OCCURRED TO ME TO WONDER *WHY* HE NEEDED *ANOTHER.* AND IF HE COULD BUY *ONE,* HE COULD BUY *OTHERS.*

PUTTING THAT WITH MAT AND PERRIN SNEAKING AROUND LIKE *BULL CALVES* PRETENDING TO BE *FOXES,* WELL, I COULD SEE ONLY ONE ANSWER.

I DON'T KNOW IF I'M *SURPRISED* OR *NOT* TO FIND YOU HERE, RAND, BUT--

I *HAVE* TO GO, EGWENE. ALL OF US DO, OR THE TROLLOCS WILL COME BACK!

DID *ANYONE* ELSE NOTICE ALL OF THIS?

AFTER LAST NIGHT, ALL THEY CAN THINK ABOUT IS REBUILDING. THAT, AND WHAT TO DO IF IT HAPPENS *AGAIN.*

THEY COULDN'T SEE ANYTHING ELSE UNLESS IT WAS PUSHED UNDER THEIR NOSES. AND I TOLD NO ONE WHAT I SUSPECTED. *NO ONE.*

HAS NO USE FOR ME NOW, WHILE ON THE OTHER HAND, I HAVE NEVER PERFORMED IN TAR VALON.

AND THOUGH I *USUALLY* JOURNEY ALONE, AFTER LAST NIGHT, I HAVE NO OBJECTIONS AT ALL TO TRAVELING IN COMPANY.

I, AH, DIDN'T THINK TO LOOK IN THE LOFT.

IS *THIS* PART OF THE PATTERN TOO, MOIRAINE SEDAI?

EVERYTHING IS PART OF THE PATTERN, MY OLD FRIEND. WE CANNOT PICK AND CHOOSE. BUT WE SHALL SEE.

NOW, WHAT HORSE FOR EGWENE?

WHAT ABOUT BELA? SHE MAY NOT BE AS FAST AS THE OTHERS, BUT SHE'S STRONG. I RIDE HER SOMETIMES. SHE CAN KEEP UP.

THEN SHE WILL HAVE TO DO. RAND, FIND A SADDLE FOR BELA. QUICKLY, NOW! WE HAVE TARRIED TOO LONG ALREADY.

They passed beyond the last farmhouses on the outskirts of the village, paralleling the North Road that led to Taren Ferry.

Rand thought surely no night sky elsewhere could be as beautiful as the sky over the Two Rivers. The clear black seemed to reach forever, with so many stars... and the moon appeared close enough to touch.

A black shape flew slowly across the silvery ball of the moon. It surprised Rand, causing him to jerk the reins involuntarily and halt his horse.

A bat, he thought, though he knew it was not. The body of it had to be as large as a man...

WHAT ARE YOU SITTING HERE AND STARING AT, BOY? WE HAVE TO KEEP MOVING.

I--I SAW... AGAINST THE MOON...

To be continued...

bonus materials

BONUS SKETCHBOOK
BY CHASE CONLEY

Ben Crowe

Aram

Bayle Damon

Bili Conqar

Balthamel

Bran

Cenn Buie

IM SO TIRED OF THATCHIN' THEEZ DAMN ROOVES...

Al'Thor House

Elaida

Elaida
(STERN.)

Ilyena

Galad Damodred

Lan

Lews Therin

Myrddraal

Min

Mordeth

Ilyena

Moiraine

Perrin

Nynaeve

Trollocs

cover gallery

Artwork by Jeremy Saliba

Artwork by Chase Conley

Artwork by Chase Conley

Artwork by Seamas Gallagher

Artwork by Chase Conley

Artwork by Seamas Gallagher

Artwork by Seamas Gallagher

Artwork by Chase Conley

Artwork by Seamas Gallagher

Artwork by Jeremy Saliba

Artwork by Jeremy Saliba

Artwork by Jeremy Saliba

Artwork by Jeremy Saliba

Artwork by Jeremy Saliba

biographies

ROBERT JORDAN

Mr. Jordan was born in 1948 in Charleston, South Carolina. He taught himself to read when he was four with the incidental aid of a twelve-years-older brother, and was tackling Mark Twain and Jules Verne by five. He was a graduate of The Citadel, the Military College of South Carolina, with a degree in physics. He served two tours in Vietnam with the U. S. Army; among his decorations are the Distinguished Flying Cross with bronze oak leaf cluster, the Bronze Star with "V" and bronze oak leaf cluster, and two Vietnamese Gallantry Crosses with palm. A history buff, he also wrote dance and theater criticism and enjoyed the outdoor sports of hunting, fishing, and sailing, and the indoor sports of poker, chess, pool, and pipe collecting. He began writing in 1977 and went on to write The Wheel of Time®, one of the most important and bestselling series in the history of fantasy publishing with over 14 million copies sold in North America, and countless more sold abroad. Robert Jordan died on September 16, 2007, after a courageous battle with the rare blood disease amyloidosis.

2008. He continues to be inspired by anime, video games, and illustration.

Chase is currently drawing *Jim Butcher's The Dresden Files*, and living and working in Charlotte, North Carolina.

NICOLAS CHAPUIS

Nicolas Chapuis was born in 1985 and decided to freelance as a comic book colorist after earning a degree in graphic design. His work includes *Robert Jordan's The Wheel of Time*, *Jonathan Stroud's Bartimaeus The Amulet of Samarkand*, and *Richard Starking's Elephantmen*.

He resides in Freiburg, Germany.

BILL TORTOLINI

Already an accomplished art director and graphic designer, Bill began lettering comics more than a decade ago and has worked with many of the comics industry's top creators and publishers.

Current and past projects include: *Stephen King's Talisman, Anita Blake: Vampire Hunter, Army of Darkness, Random Acts of Violence, Wolverine, Back to Brooklyn, The Hedge Knight, Archie Comics, Riftwar, Battlestar Galactica, The Warriors, The Wheel of Time, The Dresden Files, Transformers, Star Trek: The Next Generation, G.I. Joe, The Last Resort,* and many others.

Bill resides in Billerica, Massachusetts, with his wife and three children.